THE PHANTOM STRANGER

WALK WITH ME, AND LEARN WHAT MORTALS FEAR ABOUT DARK. WHEREVER I GO, BUT A STRANGER... THERE ARE NO SECRETS FROM ME.

THE LONGEST NIGHT

PAUL LEVITZ writer
RAÜL FERNANDEZ artist
SANTI ARCAS colorist
JOSH REED letterer
ANDREW MARINO editor

BEFORE THERE WERE CALENDARS, WHEN ALL THEY KNEW WAS SUNLIGHT GROWING SHORT AND DARKNESS LONG, FEAR ABOUNDED ON THIS DAY.

WOULD THE LIFE-GIVING WARMTH RETURN?

OR WOULD THEIR FEAR IT MIGHT NOT OPEN THE VERY GATES OF HELL?

C'MON, JIMMY!

CHILDREN DESERVE PROTECTION MORE, THEIR *INNOCENCE* A BLAZING LIGHT CALLING ME...AND THE POTENTIAL OF THEIR LIVES AHEAD *IMMEASURABLE.* HOW CAN I KNOW WHAT BEAUTY THEY MAY *GIVE* TO THE WORLD?

THERE'S GOTTA BE *MORE CANDY* OUT THERE FOR US TO GET. TRUST YOUR BIG BROTHER!

YOU KNOW BEST, CARMINE!

'AT'S A GOOD BOY!

MAYBE FATHER JOE WILL HAVE A BASKET OUT.

AS IT HAS FOR SO MANY YEARS, THE NIGHT *PASSES.* I HAVE DONE MY DUTY *AGAIN,* IN INNUMERABLE PLACES, TO PRESERVE THE INNOCENT.

I COME HERE TO WATCH THE *SUNRISE.* ODD THAT IT SHOULD FEEL SO *COMFORTABLE* HERE...

ARLINGTON NATIONAL CEMETERY

YET AM I *NOT* A WARRIOR IN THE ENDLESS BATTLE BETWEEN HEAVEN AND HELL, BOUND BY *AGELESS ORDERS* TO MY MISSION?

THERE IS MUCH THAT EVEN *I* CANNOT UNDERSTAND OR SEE, MOST OF ALL MY *OWN FATE* AND WHETHER I SHALL EVER SEE EASE.

WHY DOES THIS NIGHT OPEN THE GATE BETWEEN LIFE AND DEATH, AND WHY GIVE *ME* THE RESPONSIBILITY TO WATCH OVER IT?

REST IN
ORY

...BUT *YOU* AT LEAST SHALL KNOW THE *PEACE* OF THE GRAVE.

WHILE I...I AM TO WALK THE EARTH AS A STRANGER, KNOWING NO HOME AND NO PEACE...*FOREVER.*

WE HAVE MORE *IN COMMON* THAN MEN MIGHT *DREAM,* MY FRIEND...

NEVER THE END.

KA'AU CRATER, SOUTH SIDE.

MERMAID COVE, WEST SIDE.

THE TURTLE BAY RESORT ON THE NORTH SHORE.

THIS LAVA-ENRICHED SOIL IS AMAZING!

THERE ARE SO MANY SPECIFIC SPECIES OF PLANTS I'VE NEVER SEEN IN GOTHAM, AND YOU LITTLE GUYS ARE THRIVING OUT HERE.

DID YOU KNOW MAGNUM, P.I. WAS FILMED HERE? NOT IN THIS CAVE. DUH, IT'S FOR MERMAIDS-- WHERE ARE THE MERMAIDS ANYWAYS?

I BELIEVED IN MERMAIDS BUT I ALSO BELIEVED IN LOVE, TOO. IT'S ALL A LIEEE! UGH.

IS IT ALWAYS THIS HOT?

YES.

LIKE, EVERY DAY?

YES.

LIKE, THIS HUMID STICKY HOT?!

YESSS...

THE PUEO PROMISE

IVY, LOOK. IT'S CATWOMAN.

AND?

HEY, SYLVESTER! IT'S YOUR TWEETY BIRD!

HEY... HARLEY... HOW'S IT GOING?

PETER V. NGUYEN - writer & artist   WES ABBOTT - letterer   KATIE KUBERT - editor

A GUST OF WIND PASSES ON ITS WAY ELSEWHERE. POLLEN THREADS THE BREEZE.

PAINT CURLS AND CONCRETE CRUMBLES TO DUST.

LINOLEUM FLOORS PEEL FROM THEIR TREAD, WET AND FLIMSY, LIKE THE SKIN OF A ROTTEN APPLE.

A LOOSE WEAVE OF ROOTS REVEALS ITSELF UNDERNEATH.

TREES TURN, TWIST, AND RUMPLE THE ROADS.

YAWNING BRANCHES STRETCH AND PUSH GLASS FROM SUNKEN PANES.

A FOREST GROWS, PULLING WATER--FEEDING--FROM RUSTED PIPES.

IN EVERY PLACE, THE CURRENT OF TIME...

WHAT THE...

HEY! HELP ME, FELLAS!

HELLLLLLLL--

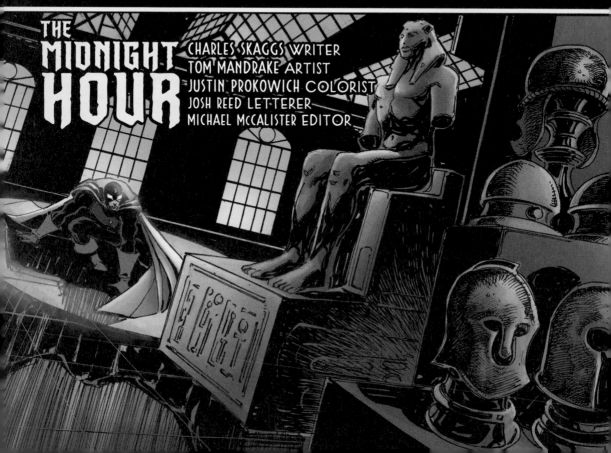

THE MIDNIGHT HOUR

CHARLES SKAGGS WRITER
TOM MANDRAKE ARTIST
JUSTIN PROKOWICH COLORIST
JOSH REED LETTERER
MICHAEL McCALISTER EDITOR

HAWKMAN? FLASH? IS ANYONE OUT THERE?

AAAAAAAAHH!

DOCTOR MID-NITE! GET ME OUT OF THIS THING, WILLYA?!

HOLD ON, ATOM!

KZZZZZSSH

SKRREEEEE!

BZZZZZ

A NEW DARKNESS

JEREMY HAUN writer • JUAN DOE art and color • ANDWORLD DESIGN letters • KATIE KUBERT editor

HMMMM. ALL RIGHT, LET'S GET TO WORK.
YOU READY?
YEAH.
READY AS I'M GOING TO BE.
THIS IS... INSANE. I'VE NEVER SEEN ANYTHING LIKE IT BEFORE.
HAVE YOU?
NO. NOT LIKE THIS.
I KNOW THIS ISN'T NECESSARILY WHAT YOU WANTED.
YEAH, IT'S CREEPY AS HELL.
NO...I MEAN, THE PROBATION-- BEING HERE WITH ME.
I LOST MY TEMPER. I...I OWN THAT.
AND NOW I'M HERE WITH YOU, KAR-VON, THE LEGENDARY WIELDER OF BOTH GREEN AND RED RINGS--THE BASTION OF BALANCE.
IN THIS WEIRD...EVIL-FEELING PLACE.
IT DOES FEEL WRONG, DOESN'T IT?
YOTH ANON PAR
A KOTH
Y A THON
Y ANON
SHUN ARA SH'ONG
SHUN ARA THON
SHUN PAR A KOTH
Y ANON

YOTH ANON PAR A KOTH
Y A THON
Y ANON

SHUN ARA SH'ONG
SHUN ARA THON

Y ANON

SHUN PAR A KOTH

Y ANON

KAR--WE HAVE TO HELP THEM.

WE NEED TO CONTACT THE CORPS *RIGHT NOW*--CALL IN BACKUP. THEN WE HELP THEM.

CHHKKKK
CHKK
CHKK

THE END.

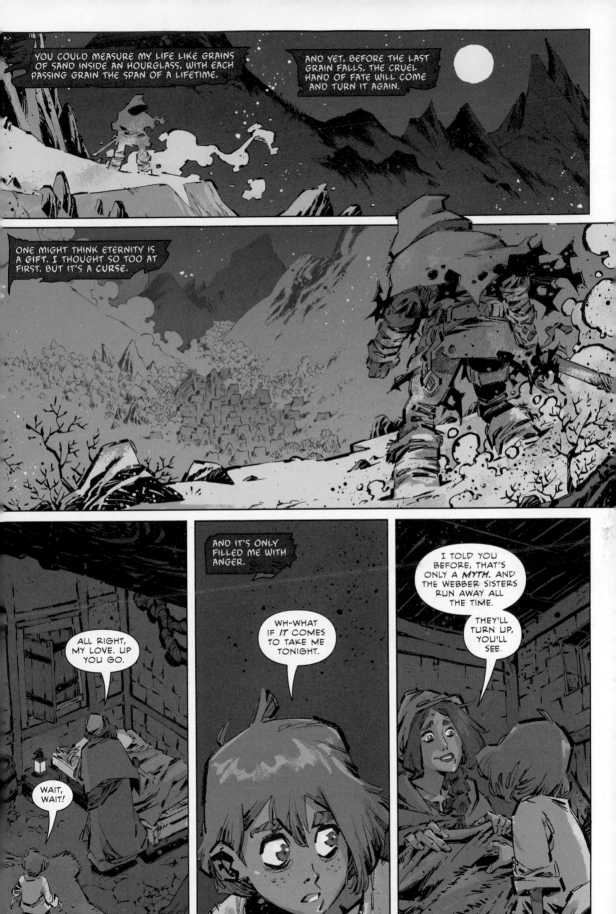

"NOTHING *CAME* FOR THEM.

I COPE BY STICKING TO THE SHADOWS.

"AH, YOU KNOW WHAT WE'LL DO?

WE'LL GET YOU YOUR *KNIGHT*.

HE'LL KEEP YOU SAFE. AND I'LL COME CHECK ON YOU IN A SHORT WHILE.

I TRY TO KEEP MY DEMONS INSIDE.

WHICH IS HARD ENOUGH TO FIGURE OUT ON ITS OWN.

AN ALE.

I DON'T KNOW YOUR FACE, FRIEND. ⸫HIC⸫ NEW ONES AROUND HERE DON'T FARE TOO WELL.

ON ACCOUNT OF THERE'S A *DEMON* IN THE SHADOWS. COMES BY NIGHT TO ⸫HIC⸫ STEAL YOU AWAY. NO ONE WANTS TO TALK ABOUT IT, BUT THEY *FEAR* IT!

DON'T MIND HIM. LAST WEEK HE WAS BABBLING ON ABOUT SOME *ETERNAL ROCK.*

GLURG

EMIL! IT TOOK EMIL!

YOU MUST HELP ME. PLEASE!

SOMEBODY.

SEE! THEY FEAR IT!

500 YEARS LATER.

ETRIGAN IN

Blood Lost and Found

MATTHEW LEVINE *writer*
JORGE CORONA *artist*
SARAH STERN *colorist*
TRAVIS LANHAM *letterer*
ANDREW MARINO *editor*

END.

YOU KNOW THE STORY.

THERE'S A CREEPY MANSION, OF COURSE.

SOME KID IS HOME ALONE.

THERE'S A NOISE DOWNSTAIRS.

A THUD. A SCRAPE.

THEN ANOTHER SOUND. RATTLING.

THE KID WANTS IT TO JUST BE THE WIND.

BUT THEN IT HAPPENS AGAIN.

CLKKKKKRTT...

IT AIN'T WIND.

IT'S SOMETHING ELSE.

SOMETHING UNINVITED.

CLKT.

IT'S THE CLASSIC HAUNTING STORY.

THE WIDE EYES. THE PANICKED RUN TO THE CLOSET WITH THE SLATTED DOOR, CHOSEN TO SERVE AS A LAST STAND.

BUT THIS PARTICULAR STORY'S GOT A TWIST IN IT.

AND IT AIN'T JUST THE APPEARANCE BY ME.

THE HAUNTING
OF WAYNE MANOR

TIM SEELEY
writer

KELLEY JONES
artist

MICHELLE MADSEN
colorist

ROB LEIGH
letterer

BEN MEARES
editor

CRAZY, MAN. I TRACK A SPIRIT ALL THE WAY FROM THE UNDERWORLD AND I END UP IN A PLACE I'VE BEEN BEFORE--

SPLDK

--RRK!

Heh. A LITERAL SILVER SPOON.

KID. WAIT...

POK

AAOW.

THIS HOUSE. I'VE BEEN HERE. IT'S *WAYNE MANOR*, THE HOME OF *BRUCE WAYNE*, WHO ALSO HAPPENS TO BE THE *BATMAN*. I KNOW.

SO THAT MAKES *YOU* A ROBIN.

BOO. I'M *DEADMAN*.

AH. Y-YES. *BOSTON BRAND*. FORMER CIRCUS ACROBAT, CURRENT SERVANT OF *RAMA KUSHNA*.

"A WOULD-BE COMEDIAN WHO TALKS OUT OF THE SIDE OF HIS MOUTH, BRAND IS NONETHELESS AN INVALUABLE SOURCE ON MATTERS OF THE AFTERLIFE, WHILE HIS ABILITY TO INHABIT LIVING BODIES CAN BE USEFUL."

FROM MY *FATHER'S* FILES.

FATHER? WAIT A SECOND, MAN...

YES. BUT I AM *NOT* A ROBIN. I AM *DAMIAN WAYNE*.

THE ROBIN.

NOW, QUICKLY, BEFORE YOU OVERSTAY YOUR WELCOME, *MR. BRAND*-- WHAT *ENTITY* DARES TRESPASS IN MY *ANCESTRAL HOME* AND WHY?

HEY, WHATEVER GETS YA THROUGH THE NIGHT, MAN. SO, WHAT WE'VE GOT IS A *LEMURE*--

OH WOW, A DUMBWAITER? SO OLD-SCHOOL RICH...

ANYWAY, A LEMURE IS A KIND OF VENGEFUL SPIRIT, WHICH I ASSUME IS COMING FOR YOUR OLD MAN. AND IT'S NOT GONNA GET CHASED OFF BY SILVERED INSTRUMENTS.

WHAT IS THE NAME OF THE SPIRIT, BRAND?

Y'KNOW, I TOLD BATMAN HE COULD AVOID THIS KIND OF THING BY THROWING BLACK BEANS AROUND THE YARD AT MIDNIGHT, BUT YOU KNOW HOW BATMAN TAKES TO ADVICE.

BRAND! THE NAME!

Hmph. HAS HE BEEN THROWING BEANS?

...I KILLED HIM.

OH.

SHOCKING, SURE. BUT THAT'S NOT THE TWIST YET.

OH, SURE. NAME'S HAZAZ SABER. RING A BELL FROM YOUR DAD'S FILES?

SABER. A MEMBER OF THE MOROCCAN MAFIA. A PRACTITIONER OF WITCHCRAFT AND AN ENEMY OF RA'S AL GHUL. I KNOW THE NAME...

THE LEMURE'S SHADOW SNEAK ATTACK AIN'T IT EITHER. BUT CHOKIN' ON ECTOPLASM ISN'T PART OF MY BALANCED BREAKFAST.

Hnh! HE'S HERE AND HIS SPIRIT'S REAL DAMN STRONG!

I CAN FEEL IT. I KNOW WHAT HE WANTS.

HE SAYS YOU TOOK HIS SOUL FROM HIS BODY, DAMIAN.

GLKKKKKFTT...

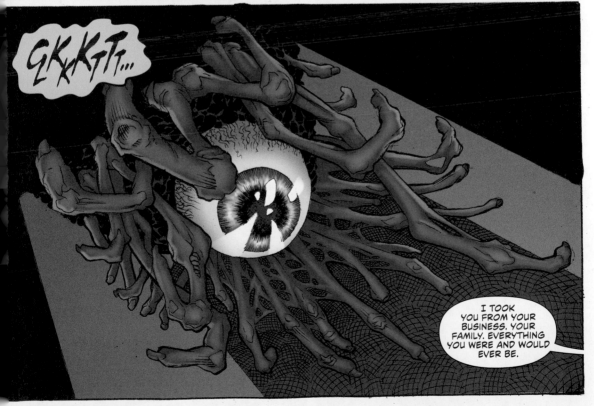

THOOM THOOM THOO

YOU ARE ANGRY. I UNDERSTAND VERY WELL.

KRAAK

BUT WHAT I DID, I DID IN SERVICE TO MY GRANDFATHER.

YOU WERE HIS COMPETITION, AND THUS YOU HAD TO BE ELIMINATED. I DIDN'T *QUESTION* IT.

CLKKKTT...

I DIDN'T KNOW *HOW* TO. UNTIL I MET MY FATHER, I BELIEVED THE WAY OF *AL GHUL* WAS THE ONLY WAY.

PLEASE, MR. SABER. I HAD LIVED ALL MY LIFE DESTINED TO SERVE RA'S AL GHUL. TO BECOME HIM.

CLKKKTT...

GAH!

KRAK

HNF!

WHAT. DID YOU BRING. INTO THE MANOR?!

BATMAN.

HE REALLY *DOES* TALK LIKE THAT. KINDA DRAGS OUT THE TERROR.

DAMIAN! ARE YOU OKAY?

OF COURSE! AM I NOT YOUR SON?

LOOK, BATS. BRUCE. I--I-- ...

I'LL SEE MYSELF OUT.

AND THERE'S THE *TWIST* I PROMISED. SEE, THE DEARLY DEPARTED SEE THINGS THE LIVING DON'T.

AND POWERFUL ENTITIES EXIST ON LEVELS *ABOVE* TIME, SQUATTIN' LIKE VULTURES ON A FENCE POST. THEIR MARKS MOVE BACKWARD 'N' FORWARD THROUGH ETERNITY.

AND IT AIN'T RA'S AL GHUL WHO HAS EYES ON DAMIAN WAYNE'S SOUL ANYMORE.

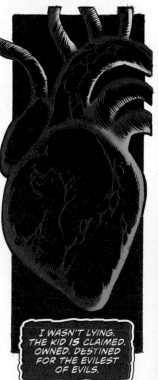

I WASN'T LYING. THE KID *IS* CLAIMED. OWNED. DESTINED FOR THE EVILEST OF EVILS.

I JUST HOPE BATMAN KNOWS WHAT *HE* INVITED INTO THE MANOR.

CUZ I AIN'T GONNA BE THE ONE TO TELL HIM.

DEADEND. FOR NEAR